THE COMPLETE PIANO PLAYER
SHOW TUNES

Arranged by Kenneth Baker

Wise Publications
London/New York/Sydney/Cologne

Exclusive distributors:
Music Sales Limited
8/9 Frith Street, London W1V 5TZ, England.
Music Sales Pty Limited
120 Rothschild Avenue, Rosebery, NSW 2018, Australia.

This book © Copyright 1989 by
Wise Publications
UK ISBN 0.7119.1693.4
Order No. AM72828

Designed by Pearce Marchbank Studio
Compiled by Peter Evans
Arranged by Kenneth Baker
Music processed by Dong – A Music Company

Music Sales' complete catalogue lists thousands of titles and is free from your local music shop, or direct from Music Sales
Limited. Please send £1 in stamps for postage to Music Sales Limited, 8/9 Frith Street, London W1V 5TZ.

Printed in the United Kingdom by
J.B. Offset Printers (Marks Tey) Limited, Marks Tey, Essex.

ANYWHERE I WANDER

Words & Music by Frank Loesser

GOODNIGHT, MY SOMEONE

Words & Music by Meredith Willson

WE KISS IN A SHADOW

Words by Oscar Hammerstein II
Music by Richard Rodgers

one   smil - ing   day   to   be   free.

To   kiss   in   the   sun - light,

and   say   to   the   sky: be - hold   and be -

lieve   what   you   see.   Be -

hold   how   my   lov - er   loves   me!

ONE HAND, ONE HEART

Music by Leonard Bernstein
Lyrics by Stephen Sondheim

SIT DOWN, YOU'RE ROCKING THE BOAT

Words & Music by Frank Loesser

TILL THERE WAS YOU

Words & Music by Meredith Willson

THE INCH WORM

Words & Music by Frank Loesser

Piano Duet

Secondo

Primo

WONDERFUL COPENHAGEN

Words & Music by Frank Loesser

NO TWO PEOPLE

Words & Music by Frank Loesser

THE SOUND OF MUSIC

Words by Oscar Hammerstein II
Music by Richard Rodgers

21

IF I WERE A BELL

Words & Music by Frank Loesser

A WONDERFUL GUY

Words by Oscar Hammerstein II
Music by Richard Rodgers

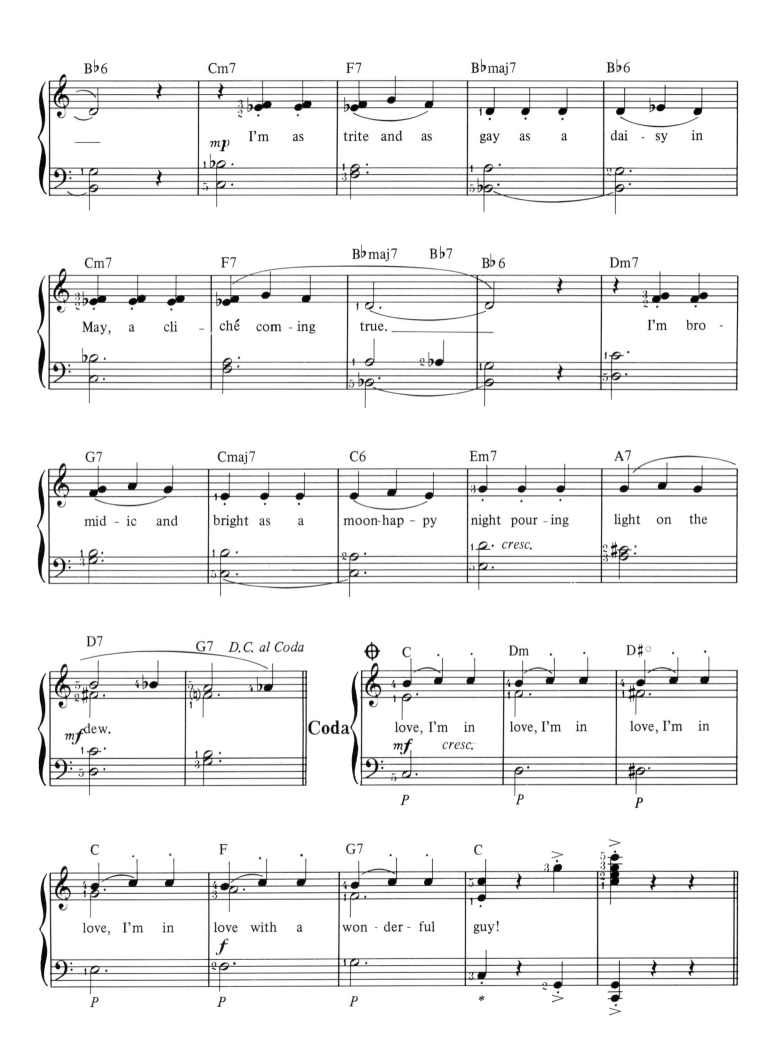

SOMEWHERE

Music by Leonard Bernstein
Lyrics by Stephen Sondheim

Rubato, with great expression ♩ = 88

There's a place for us, some-where a place for us.

Peace and qui-et and op - en air, wait for us some-where. —

There's a time for us, some-day a time for us.

Time to-geth- er with time to spare, time to learn, time to care.

I FEEL PRETTY

Music by Leonard Bernstein
Lyrics by Stephen Sondheim

A WOMAN IN LOVE

Words & Music by Frank Loesser

AMERICA

Music by Leonard Bernstein
Lyrics by Stephen Sondheim

Energetically ♩.=112

(no pedal)

I like to be in A - me - ri - ca,
Au - to - mo - bile in A - me - ri - ca,

o - kay by me in A - me - ri - ca.
chro - mi - um steel in A - me - ri - ca.

Ev - 'ry - thing free in A -
Wi - re spoke wheel in A -

me - ri - ca,
me - ri - ca,

for a small fee in A - me - ri - ca.
ve - ry big deal in A - me - ri - ca.

ONCE IN LOVE WITH AMY

Words & Music by Frank Loesser

SEVENTY SIX TROMBONES

Words & Music by Meredith Willson

39

41

I BELIEVE IN YOU

Words & Music by Frank Loesser

STANDING ON THE CORNER

Words & Music by Frank Loesser

TONIGHT

Music by Leonard Bernstein
Lyrics by Stephen Sondheim